Perry the Polar Bear GOES GREEN

A Story about Global Warming

By Olive O'Brien

Illustrated by Nina Finn-Kelcey

Perry rubbed his eyes sleepily and sat up on his ice-bed. It was early morning in the North Pole and he could hear his mother and father talking in hushed whispers.

“We need to move today,” he could hear his father saying. “The iceberg is melting fast and soon we won’t have a home.”

“We’re moving?” Perry said.

“I’m afraid so, son,” his father sighed.

“But I like it here; this is our home! And what about my toys?” Perry cried.

Perry's mother bowed down gently and scooped him up with her giant paws. "The North Pole is becoming warmer every year," she said softly. "The ice is melting faster and faster every day. Soon our iceberg will melt and completely disappear. But don't you worry, we'll find a bigger and better home."

Perry stopped crying and wiped the tears from his face.

"Now there's a brave little polar bear," his father smiled.

Perry hugged his parents and started to pack his favourite toys and teddy bears into a small bag which he carried on his back. As they dived into the icy sea, Perry turned around and took one last look at his old home.

He was old enough to swim by himself, and could proudly say that he was the best swimmer at the polar bear school. Still, after hours of travelling, Perry was exhausted. He climbed onto his father's back and was beginning to nod off, when his father yelled, "Look, there's a large iceberg! Even better, I can see seals resting on it!"

They had not eaten for weeks and a tasty seal would make a delicious dinner. They swam under the surface of the water. At the edge of the iceberg, Perry's father shot out of the sea with his sharp teeth bared, ready to grab one of the weaker seals. The polar bears were starving and they needed food straight away.

But, Perry's heart skipped a beat when he spotted a familiar figure. "Wait, it's my friend Sally Seal," he screamed. His father skidded to a stop, spraying snow everywhere.

Sally recognised Perry straight away. After all, he had helped her to find her family once, when she was lost. Perry was the only polar bear friend she ever had. They hugged each other tightly. "Perry, I'm so happy to see you," Sally said. "Why are you on this side of the North Pole?"

"Our iceberg is melting and we have to find a new home," Perry replied as he tried to blink away the tears.

"Don't worry, you can stay here for as long as you want," Sally said with a smile.

Then, the most unusual thing happened. For the first time ever, seals and polar bears sat side by side, chatting and laughing. Suddenly, Sally noticed her friend Kenny the Killer Whale.

"Hey Sally, did you hear that everyone is meeting tonight to talk about how to stop the ice melting?" he bellowed, while he splashed up and down in the sea. "The meeting will be at the biggest iceberg in the neighbourhood."

That night, polar bears from all over the North Pole gathered. They were joined by Arctic hares and foxes, along with giant walruses, killer whales and even beluga whales. The seals and beluga whales watched from afar, just in case the polar bears decided to pounce on them.

A great hush fell upon the crowd, as the King of the polar bears arrived. He was bigger than any other polar bear there, with the softest and the whitest fur. He sat on his throne and wore a crown of icicles and silver shells.

“Fellow polar bears; As many of you know, the ice is melting. Some of you have lost your homes, and two polar bears have already drowned in the sea, trying to find some ice to rest on,” the king said.

“What can we do?” one thin and hungry-looking polar bear shouted angrily. “It’s not our fault, it’s the humans’ fault.”

“I know this, but not everyone does,” the king said patiently. He went on to explain why the ice was melting. Perry and his family listened to every word. They learned that the climate was changing all over the world. The planet was becoming warmer and warmer every year. The king called it global warming.

“People are burning a lot of oil and coal to heat their homes, offices, schools and shops. They also use their cars everyday, which burns too much fuel; and they throw out a lot of garbage. All of this waste has formed a gas which has made a tent around the earth. This traps the earth’s heat,” the king explained.

”But, how does global warming affect us?” Perry’s father asked.

“Well, with all the extra heat, winters are becoming shorter here. There is less ice. More and more polar bears have to swim for longer to go from one patch of ice to another. This makes them very tired and weak. Less ice means that it is also harder for polar bears to hunt for food,” the king said. “The seals live on the ice and if there’s less ice, there are fewer hunting places for us.”

The polar bears were very angry. “Yes, we are starving,” one polar bear yelled. “Okay, we can try and catch fish or even a beluga whale, if we’re lucky, but that’s not enough!”

“But, how can we stop people all over the world from using so much energy?” a walrus shouted.

Then everyone began to shout and argue. “It’s useless just standing here and listening to everyone shouting at each other,” Perry’s mother said. Perry’s family left the meeting and started to think about where they would find their next meal. When they reached the edge of the iceberg, they stopped.

“Perry, you stay here and sit tight,” his father said. “We won’t be long, and hopefully we’ll bring back something yummy for dinner.”

Perry watched his parents swim off into the distance. He looked around at the white snow and deep blue sea. “The North Pole is such a beautiful place. Why would anyone want to destroy it?” he said to himself.

This was his last thought before he drifted off into a deep sleep. When he woke, he discovered that the ice had broken away from the iceberg during the night. He gasped when he saw that he was all alone in the middle of the sea.

Perry was terrified. After all a hungry walrus could gobble him up in one go. “Help, help,” he screamed. He could see a group of killer whales swimming in the distance. Unfortunately, not all killer whales were as friendly as Kenny and he was afraid they would eat him for dinner.

Luckily, a young boy who lived in a town nearby was out fishing and saw what had happened to Perry. Perry froze when he saw the boat approaching. If people were mean enough to cause the ice to melt, he did not want to trust this one.

The boat slowed in front of the floating ice and rocked gently to and fro. "Hi, I'm Tommy," the boy said.

"Go away, I don't need your help," Perry said glaring at him. "I would still be at home on the iceberg, if it were not for humans."

"What do you mean?" Tommy asked.

"People have caused global warming, which means that the ice is melting in the North Pole and we could lose our homes forever," Perry said.

“But you can come live with us,” Tommy said hopefully. Perry shook his head. “Polar bears like the cold; the ice is our home.”

This was the first time that Tommy had heard about the ice melting. So, Perry sat with him and explained everything. “The King of the polar bears says that if we don’t stop global warming, polar bears may disappear forever,” Perry said.

“We have to do something!” Tommy exclaimed.

“I have an idea,” Perry said with a smile. “I’m just one polar bear, in one small part of the North Pole. But if I was on TV, I could tell everyone about the ice melting. First though, I must go back to tell my parents about my plan, or they will worry about me.”

Perry climbed into the boat and they sped towards the iceberg. “I promise that I’ll help you,” Tommy said, as he dropped Perry off.

ON
OFF
RECYCLE

Tommy kept his word and he returned to Perry's home with a TV crew. Tommy and Perry appeared on the news that day.

"The ice is melting. Please help us save our home," Perry pleaded.

"We can all do our part, no matter how small it is. One person can make all the difference," Tommy said.

Perry told everyone about how they can help slow down global warming. Thousands of people learned about recycling glass bottles, plastic, paper and many other things, instead of throwing them straight into the garbage. Everyone in Tommy's town started to turn off their lights and TVs when they were not using them. This would use less energy.

The word spread quickly, and soon many people were walking or cycling to school and work, instead of using their cars every day. They even planted new trees, which would help clean the air and keep the earth cool.

The King of the polar bears was so proud of Perry. He gave him a shiny medal as a reward, which Perry wore everyday.

That night, Perry marvelled at how beautiful the Northern lights were as they danced across the sky. He trusted that people would keep doing their very best to save his beautiful home in the North Pole.

Here are some tips on how you can go green, just like Perry!

Recycle plastic, paper, glass bottles and aluminium cans.

Turn off the TV, radio, computer or light switches when you are not using them. This will use less energy.

Plant a tree. Trees turn carbon dioxide into oxygen which is good for the planet.

Walk or cycle to places that are nearby.